C000051488

$\mathcal{T}$HIS BOOK BELONGS TO:

MY PREGNANCY
Record Book
FROM PRECONCEPTION TO BIRTH

A DORLING KINDERSLEY BOOK

SP CREATIVE DESIGN
WRITER Heather Thomas
DESIGNER Rolando Ugolini

The team at Dorling Kindersley were:
SENIOR MANAGING ART EDITOR
Lynne Brown
SENIOR MANAGING EDITOR
Corinne Roberts

SENIOR ART EDITOR Karen Ward
SENIOR EDITOR Penny Warren
EDITOR Claire Cross

PRODUCTION Martin Croshaw

First published in Great Britain in 1998 by
Dorling Kindersley Limited,
9 Henrietta Street,
Covent Garden, London WC2E 8PS

Visit us on the World Wide Web at
http://www.dk.com

Copyright © 1998 Dorling Kindersley
Limited, London Text copyright © 1998
Dorling Kindersley Limited, London
except pages 4—11 © 1998 G.R. Lane
Health Products Limited

All rights reserved. No part of this
publication may be reproduced,
stored in a retrieval system, or transmitted
in any form or by any
means, electronic, mechanical,
photocopying, recording or otherwise,
without the prior written permission
of the copyright owners.

A CIP catalogue record for this book
is available from the British Library

ISBN 0–7513–0735–1

Reproduced in Italy by
GRB Editrice, Verona
Printed and bound in Italy by Lego

$\mathscr{I}$NTRODUCING THIS BOOK

THIS UNIQUE pregnancy record book is designed in an easily accessible diary format so that you can write down the details of your pregnancy in the spaces provided. Week by week, it builds up into a comprehensive personal record of how your pregnancy is progressing and how you feel at each exciting new stage.

$\mathscr{P}$REPARING FOR PREGNANCY

You will find essential information on preconceptual care and preparing for pregnancy so that you and your partner can become as fit as possible for parenthood by changing to a more healthy lifestyle.

$\mathscr{H}$EALTHY GUIDELINES

At every stage of your pregnancy, there is expert advice on how to stay fit and healthy and how to avoid some of the common complaints that are sometimes associated with pregnancy.

$\mathscr{Y}$OUR DEVELOPING BABY

Every month throughout your pregnancy, there is key information on your baby's growth and development. Understanding how your baby develops inside you will help cement the natural bonding process between you and your child.

$\mathcal{G}$ETTING READY FOR BIRTH

Throughout there are tips on preparing for labour and the arrival of your baby, including advice on how to draw up your own personal birth plan. Checklists of what to pack for labour, and useful shopping lists of baby equipment, clothes and accessories will help you to be fully prepared for the event.

$\mathcal{Y}$OUR PHOTOGRAPHIC RECORD

As well as writing down the intimate details of your pregnancy and birth experience, you can paste in photographs of your newborn baby, making this a lasting and treasured record of one of the most momentous and special times of your life.

$\mathcal{U}$SEFUL INFORMATION

At the back of the book, you will find information on maternity rights and benefits, and the addresses of health support groups.

FEELING CONFIDENT

Being informed about pregnancy will help you to be more relaxed and confident during these vital months.

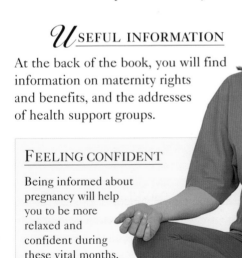

$\mathcal{C}$ONTENTS

$\mathcal{P}$LANNING FOR PREGNANCY

HAVING A BABY IS the most natural thing in the world, but there are steps you can take to help ensure your pregnancy is as healthy and happy as possible. The decision to start trying for a baby is probably the most daunting, yet exciting, that you will make. Deciding when the time is right to have a baby is a personal decision, to be taken by you and your partner.

As more women follow careers, couples are tending to delay starting a family until they have reached certain stages in their working lives. Indeed a growing number of women are waiting until their mid-thirties and beyond to have a baby. However, balancing the demands of a successful career with the knowledge that fertility decreases with age can put women under pressure. Also some couples wait until they feel financially secure before thinking about starting a family. But remember that you don't have to be a millionaire to give a baby a warm and loving home.

With the decision made, start planning at least three months before you start trying to conceive, so you are in top condition from the moment you become pregnant. If you are using the contraceptive pill, come off it now and use a condom or cap while your body settles into its natural rhythm.

Ask your GP to check your immunity to rubella (German measles). A relatively minor illness for adults, rubella can be very damaging to a developing foetus. Even if you know you've been vaccinated, it's worth checking that you are immune.

ℱOLIC ACID

Now is the time to start taking a daily folic acid supplement. Folic acid is a B vitamin that can help prevent neural tube defects, such as spina bifida, developing in the foetus. It is important that you have an adequate supply of folic acid at the time of conception, as the spinal cord is one of the first parts of a foetus to develop.

Folic acid can be found in a variety of foods, including Brussels sprouts, spinach, broccoli and wholemeal bread. However, it is difficult to obtain the required daily amount of folic acid from food alone. For example, you would need to eat five portions of Brussels sprouts every day to get enough! Folic acid can also be lost when food is stored for a long time or overcooked.

The Department of Health recommends that along with increasing your intake of foods that are high in folic acid, you should also take a 400 microgram supplement every day as soon as you decide you want to become pregnant. If there is a family history of neural tube defects, or if you are epileptic, you will need a higher dose of folic acid, which is available only on prescription. Ask your GP for advice before trying to conceive. As well as taking folic acid before conception, you must take it for the first 12 weeks of your pregnancy to help give your baby the best possible start in life.

LANES PRECONCEIVE

Lanes Preconceive provides the daily recommended amount of folic acid in easy-to-swallow tablet form. In line with Department of Health recommendations, Preconceive contains only folic acid, and each packet provides three months' supply.

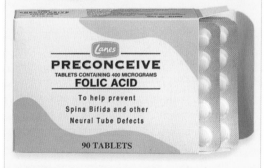

LANES PRECONCEIVE *is available from pharmacists, supermarkets and health food stores.*

THE IMPORTANCE
OF EXERCISE

*W*HAT SORT OF EXERCISE?

You don't need to belong to an expensive gym to exercise regularly. Instead, you could try some brisk walking or swimming at least three times a week. If you attend a keep-fit or aerobics class, tell your instructor as soon as you become pregnant, and check that he or she is properly qualified to teach you. You may have to modify your normal exercise programme and cut out any aerobics and jerky movements.

However, you should remember that there are certain forms of exercise, such as riding and skiing, that are not recommended for pregnant women. If you are at all unsure, check with your doctor or midwife first.

YOU ARE MORE LIKELY to enjoy your pregnancy if you are relatively fit. This doesn't mean that you have to be an Olympic athlete! If you exercise regularly, you should continue to do so throughout the time when you are trying to conceive and once you are pregnant.

My weekly exercise plan

STRETCHING EXERCISES
Gently tilt your head over to one side. Lift your chin and rotate your head to the other side and down. Repeat, starting on the other side. With your head straight, turn it slowly to the left, then back to the middle and then to the right. Repeat.

YOUR PARTNER'S HEALTH

Encourage your partner to get fit and stay fit with you. His level of fitness can affect the quality of his sperm. If your partner is exercising regularly, you both are more likely to stick to a healthy regime. Be aware that a poor diet or too much alcohol can lead to a lower sperm count, so explain to him that what he drinks and eats matters just as much as your diet.

PUTTING YOUR FEET UP

Taking time out to relax will bring huge benefits. If you stand for much of the day, relieve tired feet by lying on your back, hugging your knees into your chest.

Remember *Make sure you tell your exercise instructor when you become pregnant.*

WEIGHT LOSS

Weight-loss diets are not a good idea for pregnant women. They may deprive your body of vital nutrients and could also affect your fertility and general health. If you do want to lose weight, make sure that you go on a diet *before* you start trying for a baby.

HEALTH TIPS

HEALTHY NUTRITIONAL FOODS

A balanced diet is essential for keeping you in the best possible shape, and for providing your unborn child with the right start in life. Eat fruit and vegetables raw, or steam them, to preserve a high level of vitamins and minerals, and make sure you eat a balance of different types of food — proteins, carbohydrates and fats. A varied diet of meat, fish, dairy foods, wholegrain cereals, fruit and vegetables will supply everything you need.

WATER OR FRUIT JUICES
Always choose water or unsweetened fruit juices instead of alcoholic drinks. Reduce the amount of alcohol you drink — or, better still, cut it out altogether if you can.

FOLIC ACID
Take a 400 microgram supplement of folic acid every day from the moment you start trying for a baby until you are 12 weeks pregnant.

EVEN BEFORE YOU BECOME pregnant, you can adopt a healthier lifestyle to maximize your chances of having a smooth pregnancy and a healthy baby.

My diet

....

....

....

....

....

....

....

FOODS TO AVOID

It is advisable to avoid certain foods once you are pregnant. In case you become pregnant sooner than you expect, choose safer alternatives now. Watch out for the following foods:
- Soft, unpasteurized cheeses and liver pâtés, because they can cause listeriosis.
- Raw or lightly-cooked eggs, which may contain salmonella.
- Liver, because it contains high levels of vitamin A, which can be harmful to an unborn baby.

Problems resulting from eating these foods are rare, but they can occur, so it's best to try to avoid them. Make sure that your food is always thoroughly cooked, especially chicken and pre-prepared meals.

Remember *If you both want to maximize your chances of having a healthy baby, you should give up smoking now. Don't wait until you are pregnant.*

HOUSEHOLD PETS

If you have a cat, then ask someone else to change the litter tray if possible, or wear rubber gloves if you have to do it yourself. Toxoplasmosis, an organism found in cat and dog faeces, as well as in raw meat, can affect pregnant women, and if the infection is passed on to the unborn child, it can cause serious birth defects.

RELAXATION

Try to take time out to relax at this important time in your life. Avoid taking on too much to keep your stress levels at a minimum.

AVOID STRESS
Make time every day to relax – just sitting quietly or reading can reduce tension.

HOW LIFE BEGINS

ℱERTILIZATION

After each egg is released from the ovary, it is guided into the Fallopian tube which connects to the uterus (womb). As the egg moves down the Fallopian tube towards the uterus, the womb lining begins to thicken. This is the time in your monthly cycle when you are most fertile — the ideal time to have sexual intercourse in order to conceive.

During intercourse, the man releases hundreds of millions of sperm. Some of these will swim up the vagina, through the neck of the uterus — the cervix — into the womb and on to the Fallopian tubes.

Once in the Fallopian tubes, the sperm may intercept the egg that is travelling down towards the uterus. If the sperm successfully penetrates the egg and fertilizes it, you will become pregnant.

The fertilized egg then travels down the Fallopian tube into the uterus, where it attaches itself firmly to the thickened lining and starts to develop into a foetus. You have created a unique human being.

EVERY WOMAN IS BORN WITH a lifetime's supply of eggs, which are stored in the two ovaries. From the onset of puberty — when menstruation begins — these eggs start to be released, usually one each month. This process is called ovulation.

Notes on my menstrual cycle
....

....

....

....

....

....

....

FERTILIZATION OF THE EGG

5 Fertilized egg (zygote)

6 Dividing zygote forms a solid ball of cells

7 The zygote implants in the uterine wall

4 Sperm fertilizes the egg

3 Fimbriae collect the ripe eggs

1 Ovary produces eggs

2 Egg follicle releases an egg

AREA SHOWN IN CROSS-SECTION

BOY OR GIRL?

Each egg contains a single X chromosome, whereas a sperm may have an X or a Y chromosome. An egg fertilized by an X sperm will create a girl; if fertilized by a Y sperm, it will develop into a baby boy.

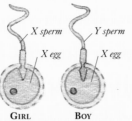

X sperm *Y sperm*

X egg *X egg*

GIRL **BOY**

*I*NCREASING THE ODDS

If you are trying for a baby, work out when you are most likely to ovulate. In a regular 28-day menstrual cycle, this will probably be about 12 to 16 days before your next period. Sperm can survive in a woman's body for several days, so the ideal time to have intercourse is the day before you ovulate, because this gives the sperm the maximum possible time to travel into the Fallopian tubes to find the ripe egg.

KNOW YOUR BODY
Every woman's cycle is different, so you need to get to know your own body pattern to work out when you are likely to ovulate. You might find it helpful to use an ovulation-testing kit to find out precisely when you are ovulating. Knowing this could increase your chances of becoming pregnant.

CHANCES OF SUCCESS
No two couples are the same when it comes to having a baby. Some pregnancies happen almost immediately, while others take longer — both are normal. Only half of the couples who are trying for a baby are successful within the first six months. On average, you have a 90 percent chance of getting pregnant within a year.

11

Now You Are PREGNANT

CONGRATULATIONS! Now that your pregnancy has been confirmed, you can embark on an exciting new chapter in your life. This is the special moment for which you and your partner have been waiting. During the next few weeks, your body will start adjusting to being pregnant and you may experience a wide range of unfamiliar and often conflicting feelings. Even though you won't look pregnant yet, the increased hormonal activity in your body may activate sudden mood swings and appetite changes. Don't worry — this is perfectly normal, and you will probably be walking around on cloud nine for days to come.

One of the first decisions that you must make is whom you should tell and when you should do so. This is entirely a matter of personal choice. Obviously, you will tell your partner, and possibly your immediate family, as soon as you know yourself. However, some women delay telling their friends for a few weeks, possibly until the end of the first trimester (at 12 weeks).

YOU'RE PREGNANT! Discovering that you are pregnant can be very exciting for both you and your partner.

You should tell your employer that you are pregnant before you attend your first antenatal clinic, which will probably be at about three months. You should get in contact with your doctor as soon as possible in order to discuss the range of different birth options and antenatal care. There are many choices to make about labour and birth and you should be aware of all the available options before making up your mind.

YOUR ESTIMATED DATE OF DELIVERY

To work out your due date, find the first day of your last period next to the months in heavy type. The date below is your estimated delivery date.

JANUARY 1 2 3 4 5 6 7 8 9 10 11 12 13 14 15 16 17 18 19 20 21 22 23 24 25 26 27 28 29 30 31
Oct/Nov   8 9 10 11 12 13 14 15 16 17 18 19 20 21 22 23 24 25 26 27 28 29 30 31 *1 2 3 4 5 6 7*

FEBRUARY 1 2 3 4 5 6 7 8 9 10 11 12 13 14 15 16 17 18 19 20 21 22 23 24 25 26 27 28
Nov/Dec   *8 9 10 11 12 13 14 15 16 17 18 19 20 21 22 23 24 25 26 27 28 29 30* 1 2 3 4 5

MARCH 1 2 3 4 5 6 7 8 9 10 11 12 13 14 15 16 17 18 19 20 21 22 23 24 25 26 27 28 29 30 31
Dec/Jan   6 7 8 9 10 11 12 13 14 15 16 17 18 19 20 21 22 23 24 25 26 27 28 29 30 31 *1 2 3 4 5*

APRIL 1 2 3 4 5 6 7 8 9 10 11 12 13 14 15 16 17 18 19 20 21 22 23 24 25 26 27 28 29 30
Jan/Feb   6 7 8 *9 10 11 12 13 14 15 16 17 18 19 20 21 22 23 24 25 26 27 28 29 30 31* 1 2 3 4

MAY 1 2 3 4 5 6 7 8 9 10 11 12 13 14 15 16 17 18 19 20 21 22 23 24 25 26 27 28 29 30 31
Feb/Mar   5 6 7 8 9 10 11 12 13 14 15 16 17 18 19 20 21 22 23 24 25 26 27 28 *1 2 3 4 5 6 7*

JUNE 1 2 3 4 5 6 7 8 9 10 11 12 13 14 15 16 17 18 19 20 21 22 23 24 25 26 27 28 29 30
Mar/Apr   *8 9 10 11 12 13 14 15 16 17 18 19 20 21 22 23 24 25 26 27 28 29 30 31* 1 2 3 5 6 7

JULY 1 2 3 4 5 6 7 8 9 10 11 12 13 14 15 16 17 18 19 20 21 22 23 24 25 26 27 28 29 30 31
Apr/May   7 8 9 10 11 12 13 14 15 16 17 18 19 20 21 22 23 24 25 26 27 28 29 30 *1 2 3 4 5 6 7*

AUGUST 1 2 3 4 5 6 7 8 9 10 11 12 13 14 15 16 17 18 19 20 21 22 23 24 25 26 27 28 29 30 31
May/June   *8 9 10 11 12 13 14 15 16 17 18 19 20 21 22 23 24 25 26 27 28 29 30 31* 1 2 3 4 5 6 7

SEPTEMBER 1 2 3 4 5 6 7 8 9 10 11 12 13 14 15 16 17 18 19 20 21 22 23 24 25 26 27 28 29 30
June/July   8 9 10 11 12 13 14 15 16 17 18 19 20 21 22 23 24 25 26 27 28 29 30 *1 2 3 4 5 6 7*

OCTOBER 1 2 3 4 5 6 7 8 9 10 11 12 13 14 15 16 17 18 19 20 21 22 23 24 25 26 27 28 29 30 31
July/Aug   *8 9 10 11 12 13 14 15 16 17 18 19 20 21 22 23 24 25 26 27 28 29 30 31* 1 2 3 4 5 6 7

NOVEMBER 1 2 3 4 5 6 7 8 9 10 11 12 13 14 15 16 17 18 19 20 21 22 23 24 25 26 27 28 29 30
Aug/Sep   8 9 10 11 12 13 14 15 16 17 18 19 20 21 22 23 24 25 26 27 28 29 30 31 *1 2 3 4 5 6*

DECEMBER 1 2 3 4 5 6 7 8 9 10 11 12 13 14 15 16 17 18 19 20 21 22 23 24 25 26 27 28 29 30 31
Sep/Oct   7 8 *9 10 11 12 13 14 15 16 17 18 19 20 21 22 23 24 25 26 27 28 29 30* 1 2 3 4 5 6 7

$\mathcal{F}$ERTILIZATION

Fertilization takes place in the Fallopian tube when a sperm penetrates the tough outer membrane of an egg. Once inside the oocyte (the egg's innermost part), the sperm sheds its tail and joins its chromosomes to those of the egg. The fertilized egg cells then divide repeatedly until a blastocyst (a hollow ball of cells) is formed and implants itself in the uterus. At this stage, the pregnancy is established.

A FERTILIZED EGG DIVIDES RAPIDLY

$\mathcal{S}$IGNS OF PREGNANCY

- You will miss a period.
- Your breasts will feel heavier and more sensitive.
- The nipple area will deepen in colour.
- You may feel very tired.
- You may pass urine more frequently.
- You may feel nauseous, especially early in the morning.
- You may crave certain foods and some foods may taste odd.
- Your sense of smell may be more acute.

WEEK 1

Date

My thoughts and feelings

WEEK 2

Date

My thoughts and feelings

Remember Don't wait for your pregnancy to be confirmed. Improve your lifestyle now!

14

USING A PREGNANCY TEST KIT

You can use a pregnancy test kit at home to test a sample of your urine. Most kits work in a similar way to the one shown below. Just hold the absorbent pad of the test wand in your urine stream for a few seconds. Replace the wand in the cartridge and check the results windows after the specified time. For a positive result, both windows will show a colour. The absorbent wand reacts if a hormone produced by the embryo is present in your urine.

Results window | Cartridge | Absorbent pad | Test wand

WEEK 3

Date

My thoughts and feelings

WEEK 4

Date

My thoughts and feelings

ESSENTIAL NUTRIENTS

You provide the food your baby needs to develop and grow, so you must eat a varied, balanced diet. You need:

- PROTEIN Choose chicken, fish, red meat, eggs, lentils, nuts and dairy products.
- CARBOHYDRATES Opt for unrefined ones, such as wholegrain cereals, rice, beans and pasta. They are all good sources of fibre.
- CALCIUM You need twice as much when pregnant for building the baby's bones and teeth. Eat cheese, milk, yogurt and green vegetables.
- IRON During pregnancy you need extra iron. Eat lean red meat, spinach, dried apricots and fish. Increase your intake of vitamin C to aid iron absorption.
- FOLIC ACID Needed for the baby's developing central nervous system. Make sure that you eat plenty of fresh, dark-green vegetables, broccoli, nuts, seeds and wholemeal bread.

FRESH FRUIT
This is a good source of the vitamins and minerals your baby needs for growth.

WEEK 5

Date

My thoughts and feelings

21st October 99
Did a pregnanty test
today. Possotive

WEEK 6

Date

My thoughts and feelings

Woke up bleeding, went to
hospital for a scan
everything is O.K. I saw your
heart beeting. You are wonderful
28th October 99 6 weeks 1½
at noon today.
Remember Continue taking your folic
acid tablets until week twelve.

16

Date

My thoughts and feelings

Moved into Wear house 30/10/99
I am feeling very sick.
I am eating like a horse.
I am tyred like never
before.

Date

My thoughts and feelings

8th November 99
midwife at 2.30.
I didn't see my midwife
and on the whole I did
not find her very helpfull,
as I have so many
questions about what
haveing you is going to do
to me.

CONFIRMATION OF PREGNANCY

When your pregnancy has been confirmed you should see your family doctor for a check-up and discuss your pregnancy care and the options available to you. Now is the time to find out as much as possible about pregnancy and to ask any questions you may have about your health, labour and delivery. An appointment will be made to attend your first antenatal clinic, usually at your local hospital.

YOUR BABY

At eight weeks, the foetus is starting to look human, with rudimentary hands and fingers, and feet with toes. The eyes are formed but the eyelids are still closed over them. Already the basic structure of all the major organs is in place, although the foetus is only about 3cm (1¹/₄in) long. The heart has all four chambers and beats about 180 times per minute.

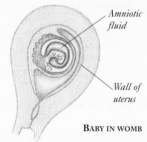

Amniotic fluid

Wall of uterus

BABY IN WOMB

$\mathcal{U}$NUSUAL FOOD CRAVINGS

Rising hormone levels can affect your saliva, making you crave some foods and dislike the taste of others. Don't worry if you suddenly develop a fancy for pickled onions. But try to control yearnings for fatty or sugary foods that are high in calories and low in nutrients.

$\mathcal{M}$ORNING SICKNESS

Feeling nauseous is common in early pregnancy but it usually disappears after the twelfth week. A dry biscuit or some toast may help to counteract nausea, especially first thing in the morning when your blood sugar levels may be low after a long night's sleep. Avoid eating rich, fried and spicy foods — eat small, bland meals and snacks frequently throughout the day.

WEEK 9

Date

My thoughts and feelings

The house isn't finished and I feel very sick still. I am working part time now and need a sleep every day.

WEEK 10

Date

My thoughts and feelings

I feel very sick, weak and tyred. I need to sleep alot. I hope this house is finished soon.

WEEK 11

Date

My thoughts and feelings

30th November 99
I had a scan at the galleries health ± center. I was date at 11 ½ weeks. You looked just beautiful, so perfect.

WEEK 12

Date

My thoughts and feelings

Saturday 4th Dec
12 weeks today.

Remember Feelings of nausea will soon disappear as you enter your second trimester.

YOU & YOUR BABY

YOU will now be starting to feel pregnant and, although you will not yet be visibly pregnant to other people, you will probably begin to gain weight as the baby grows rapidly inside you.

YOUR BABY will now look much more human with more clearly defined features. At 12 weeks, he has nearly completed the early phase of his development and can now get on with growing. Floating comfortably in a warm sac of amniotic fluid, his bones are developing rapidly and his eyelids are forming. Although he is very active and wriggles a lot, you will not feel his movements yet. He receives vital nourishment via the rich network of blood vessels in the placenta.

BABY IN WOMB

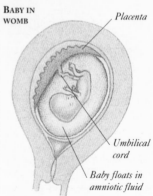

Placenta

Umbilical cord

Baby floats in amniotic fluid

WEIGHT AND LENGTH
Your baby now weighs about 48g (1.7oz) and is about 6cm (2.5in) long from crown to rump.

WEEK 13

Date **1 3rd Dec 1999**

My thoughts and feelings

Because the consultant changed my due date the number of weeks pregnant I am has canged. I am now one week ferther on in the pregnancy.

WORKING DURING PREGNANCY

You can continue working during your pregnancy. When you give up work depends on how you feel, how far you have to travel, and how stressful your work is. Many women work right up to their due date! Check your working environment to ensure that there is nothing that could put you or your baby at risk. At work, you should sit down as much as possible.

Remember Tell your employer that you are pregnant and when you plan to stop working.

Date 1**8**th Dec 1999

My thoughts and feelings

I am starting to feel better, a little less sick. I still get tyred, but I am feeling a lot happier now I'm not feeling so sick.

YOUR FIRST ANTENATAL CHECK-UP

You will be asked about your general health, medical history and your pregnancy. You may also be given an internal examination. The following tests will be carried out:

- Measuring your height.
- Noting your weight.
- Testing your urine.
- Testing your blood.
- Monitoring the baby's heartbeat.
- Examining your breasts.
- Checking your blood pressure.

PLANNING YOUR EXERCISE PROGRAMME

It's a good idea to plan an exercise programme that you can continue throughout your pregnancy. You may have to moderate your exercise programme as your "bump" gets larger, but even then you can continue with gentle stretching and toning exercises. Regular exercise can help build strength and stamina for labour and maintain muscle tone and flexibility.

THE ANGRY CAT
This exercise eases tired, aching back muscles. Kneel with your arms and legs in line, supporting your weight evenly. Slowly raise your back, dropping your head and shoulders. Breathe out, pulling in your pelvic floor muscles. Inhale slowly and relax.

Keep your hands and knees in line

WHERE THE POUNDS GO

The average weight gain during pregnancy is 28lb (14kg). Mothers who put on this much weight and eat a healthy, nutritious diet tend to have healthy babies and fewer complications. The table below shows how all the extra weight is accounted for:

	pounds
• baby	7½
• enlarged uterus	2
• placenta	1½
• amniotic fluid	2
• enlarged breasts	1½
• increased blood volume	4
• increased body fluid & fat	9½
Total weight gain:	**28**

EATING FOR TWO

Although you are now eating for two, it's quality, not quantity, that counts. To cope with the increased demands of pregnancy, you should eat a highly nutritious diet.

• Eat plenty of fibre-rich foods to avoid getting constipation and piles.
• Avoid "empty" calories, found in cakes, biscuits, creamy desserts and chocolate.
• Eat plenty of fresh fruit and vegetables every day.
• Enjoy a nutritious snack of low-fat yogurt or fruit.
• Don't eat more just because you are pregnant.

WEEK

15

Date 27th Dec 1999

My thoughts and feelings

25th December 99 saturday Sarah + Richard have come up for christmas. We have all had a lovely christmas, its the first xmas dinner I have been pleased with. It mite have had something to do with the fact I have not drank any alcohol. Lots of christmas wishis for you! I look forward to next year and all the rest with you.

Remember You may be eating for two, but you don't have to eat twice as much food!

22

WEEK 16

Date 31st Dec 1999

My thoughts and feelings

1st January 2000

I was 16 week on the 1st of January 2000 You are our new year toast at 12 o'clock Matthew, Rebecca Mum and Dad all wish for the safe arivals of you. I look forward to seeing you.

YOUR FIRST SCAN

When you have an ultrasound scan, you can see your unborn baby on the screen. It is exciting when you see your baby for the first time. To the untrained eye, a scan may appear blurred but the operator will help you to distinguish the shapes and images on the screen. Scans are done to monitor your baby's progress and check on her health. A routine ultrasound scan will reveal the following:

- The baby's position.
- The baby's growth rate.
- The development of the placenta.
- Whether you are expecting more than one baby.

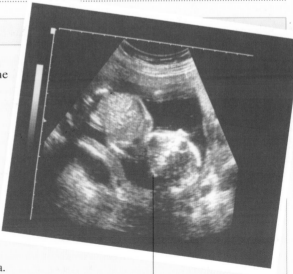

Foetus can move around freely in amniotic fluid

Date 7th Jan

My thoughts and feelings

feeling much better. I look quite pregnant now, I rather like my new bump. I am recovering from all the guests at christmas and starting to settle back into normal life again

SPORTS YOU CAN ENJOY DURING PREGNANCY

Just because you are pregnant does not mean that you have to stop exercising and put your feet up for nine months. You can continue to enjoy:

- Swimming
- Walking briskly
- Aquaerobics
- Dancing
- Yoga and stretching

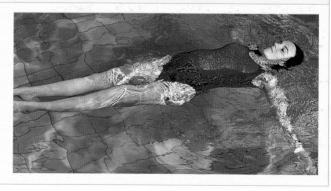

Date 12th Jan 2000

My thoughts and feelings

I saw the midwife this week and she said everything is fine. She measured my tummy and I am 18cm at 18 weeks, perfect. I feel so very much better now I have more energy and only a little tired It was Tom's birthday this week on the 16th we went out for dinner at Quinceys.

Remember To learn more about childbirth and parenting skills, enrol in an antenatal class.

ANTENATAL CLASSES

Now is the time to enrol. Classes vary in their styles of teaching so it is a good idea to shop around. Good classes include:
- Practising relaxation.
- Breathing for labour.
- Practising positions for labour.
- Rehearsing with your partner.
- Discussing your feelings.
- Learning about breastfeeding.

PREGNANCY HORMONES AND THEIR EFFECTS

During pregnancy, new hormones are produced by your body, and the production of existing hormones increases.
- PROGESTERONE is important for maintaining the pregnancy and relaxing certain muscles in the body.
- OESTROGEN stimulates the development of milk glands, and strengthens the womb wall in readiness for labour.
- PROLACTIN helps produce breast milk.
- OXYTOCIN stimulates contractions in labour.

CHOOSING A NEW WARDROBE

By now, your waistline will be expanding and many of your favourite clothes will feel uncomfortably tight. Start thinking about your wardrobe for the coming months. Maternity clothes are loose and comfortable, and flattering to your burgeoning figure. You don't need to buy lots of expensive clothes. Invest in a few standard items that can be worn with loose shirts, T-shirts, sweaters and jackets.

- **Maternity dress** A loose, flowing dress is useful for special occasions, and could double up for work if it is quite smart.
- **Trousers** You can buy smart trousers or even jeans with an expandable front panel for comfort.
- **Loose tops** Most loosely cut shirts, tunics, jackets and sweaters can continue to be worn after pregnancy.
- **Skirts and culottes** Like trousers, these can be bought with expanding waist bands or stretchy front panels.
- **Shoes** Flat or low-heeled shoes are sensible as you get bigger and more unstable.
- **Underwear** You will need a properly fitted, supportive bra with adjustable straps for comfort. Maternity tights give a lot of support; they are available in many shades.

WEEK 19

Date 21th Jan

My thoughts and feelings Whent to the hospital for a scan. You were very busy, it was supposed to to take 20 minute but it took 40 because you would not keep still, they couldn't get youre head measurment because you kept moving or hiding behind my belly butt When they turned the monitor around so we could see, yo were moving every where you pushed every part of youre body up to show us. It was very lovely I was so very happ to, see you looking so well.

Remember You don't have to spend a fortune on maternity clothes — just buy a few classic items.

WEEK 20

Date **28**th Jan

My thoughts and feelings It's my birthday on saturday 29th Jan. We went out to find a Xcountred push chair on the saturday. We have found one we like very much. on the sunday we went to the glass works really good we saw someone making a staned glass window and some else etching glass and how they make the glass is interesting too.

YOU & YOUR BABY

YOU are now well into your second trimester and are probably feeling better than ever. Any feelings of nausea should have disappeared, and you are fired up with new energy. Your waistline is disappearing and you may notice the appearance of stretch marks.

YOUR BABY is now well developed but cannot yet survive outside the uterus because her lungs and digestive system are still immature. She will probably move in response to any pressure that is applied to your abdomen. She can hear the pounding of your pulse, the murmuring of the placenta, and even your voice. Many of her "baby" teeth have formed already, hidden in her gums.

BABY IN WOMB

Body is covered by fine, downy hair (lanugo)

YOUR BABY'S MOVEMENTS

At 20 weeks, your baby has developed a nervous system and muscles that allow her to move around inside the womb. She stretches, turns, waves her arms and swims around in the warm amniotic fluid. It is an amazing experience when you feel her moving inside you for the first time. At first, your baby's movements will feel like little fluttering butterfly sensations in your tummy but they will soon get stronger and more noticeable — this is known as "quickening".

WEIGHT AND LENGTH
Your baby will measure about 18.5cm (7.5in) from crown to rump and weigh around 0.5kg (1lb).

ℛELAX WITH YOGA

Practising yoga on a regular basis throughout pregnancy can promote good health in both you and your unborn child. Yoga exercises are calming and help reduce the effects of stress, as well as easing aches and pains, especially in your back. Women who do yoga often find that they have easy, shorter labours. If you are already a yoga devotee, continue with your normal postures, performing them slowly and gently, but stop if you feel any discomfort. If you have not done yoga before, find an experienced instructor who can adapt the exercises to accommodate your enlarging abdomen.

RELAXATION

For total relaxation in yoga, lie on your back with your feet 60cm (2ft) apart, toes turned out, and arms loosely at your sides. Close your eyes and roll your head gently from side to side. Stretch out your arms and hands, palms upwards. Relax your whole body and stay like this for about 10 minutes.

WEEK 21

Date 28th Jan 4 Feb

My thoughts and feelings

I feel quite well at the moment. I do get tired but otherwise I am O.K. I am enjoying beeing pregnant now.

Remember Relaxation is important — put aside some time to rest every day.

Date 11th Feb

My thoughts and feelings

Another good week.

very much

CARING FOR YOUR BABY

You can now probably feel your baby moving inside you and these movements will get stronger as the weeks go by. Already he can taste and smell, and hear and respond to noises outside the womb. He can even experience your emotions due to the release of chemicals, such as endorphins, so why not talk to him, play soothing music, and gently touch and rub your abdomen? It will help you to get to know and feel close to your baby.

MOVING WELL

Good posture and moving well can help prevent backache. As you get bigger, your weight can throw you off-balance, causing you to lean backwards to compensate and thereby straining your lower back. Instead, when standing you should lengthen and straighten your back to centre the weight of the baby. Drop your shoulders, tuck in your bottom and lift your chest and ribs. Wear low heels and listen to your body when walking, sitting or lifting.

LIFTING SOMETHING HEAVY
Bending your knees, crouch down, keeping your back straight. Hold the weight close in to your body as you lift it up, slowly and smoothly.

$\mathcal{M}$AKING A BIRTH PLAN

Even though you still have some months to go, you should start thinking about making a birth plan. Write down the sort of birth you would like, with special reference to labour procedures, pain-killing drugs and how you wish to feed your baby. Discuss it with your doctor and midwife to find out what is feasible. For more information on birth plans, turn to page 50.

WEEK
23

Date **18**th feb

My thoughts and feelings We are going down to Eastbourne next weekend for Sarah's 50th birthday. I remember we hadn't got her present jet and had to phone Tom at work e the sunday so we could go and get it. Tom's worked all weekend after being away last week I hope he's not over doing it.

AVOIDING VARICOSE VEINS

There is a greater risk of developing varicose veins if you are very overweight or if they run in your family. If you stand for too long, your legs may ache and the veins may bulge as blood pools in the legs. To help avoid varicose veins, follow the guidelines below:

- Wear support tights.
- Rest with your feet up.
- Don't eat too much salt.
- Do gentle daily exercise.

PUT YOUR FEET UP
Raise your legs and feet when you are resting.

Place a cushion under your feet for extra comfort

Date **25th** Feb

My thoughts and feelings We went to Eastbourne on the 24th Thursday. We stayed with Sarah and Richard, exept for the friday night which was at Sadies. Tom has to come back in 5 weeks to have his tooth redun. We had a very busy time in Eastbourne. Tom went out with Mark on the Saturday, I went and saw Sarra + Mandy, Cherrie + Mark nd Abbie + Shaun. I missed Sarah on the sunday we went nd saw Tom Nan and had inner at the Star.

Remember *If you suffer from heartburn, eat smaller meals more frequently.*

YOU & YOUR BABY

YOU will now be gaining weight at the rate of about 0.5kg (1lb) per week. Your baby is now beginning to press upwards on your stomach and you may get indigestion or heartburn. You should feel your baby moving several times every day.

YOUR BABY is growing slowly but steadily and will soon start to put some weight on her bony frame. Her arms and legs now have their normal amount of muscle. As she gets larger, she takes up more and more of the uterus. Air sacs are forming inside her lungs.

BABY IN WOMB

Skin is wrinkled

Body still thin but in proportion to head

WEIGHT AND LENGTH
Your baby now weighs just under 1kg (2lb) and measures about 25cm (10in) from crown to rump.

<table>
<tr><td>
WEEK
25
</td><td>
Date ~~25th Feb~~ 3rd March
</td></tr>
</table>

My thoughts and feelings I am very tired from the weekend. We got some nice things for the baby when we were there. A mosses basket, ~~and~~ bouncy chair, back pack carrie all second hand, I am very pleased. It was lovely to see every one but I'm very glad to be home. I feel quite well and active.

Remember *Take care of your skin by using fragrant oils and moisturising creams.*

RELAX WITH MASSAGE

A soothing massage can help relieve stress and ease away feelings of tiredness. It relaxes aching muscles, particularly in your lower back, and improves your circulation. Massage can be a shared pleasure with your partner.

A SOOTHING TOUCH
If wished, to reduce friction between hands and skin, you can use a specially formulated massage oil or a suitable aromatherapy oil.

LOWER BACK MASSAGE
To relieve backache, ask your partner to gently massage the lower back and the base of your spine with the heels of the hands.

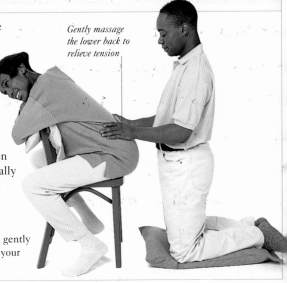

Gently massage the lower back to relieve tension

Date 6th March

My thoughts and feelings Pauline + Andy came round for dinner a very nice evening. We also have painted the bathroom and babys room. Very please with both. We have ~~to~~ brought most of the thing we need for the ~~b~~dy now. We've ~~go~~t reusable nappies and clothes and all the little things for ~~th~~ you. We are ~~g~~eting the cot neat sunday when mother care have got me money off.

Remember Take care only to use massage oils that are safe for pregnant women.

MINIMIZING STRETCH MARKS

Most pregnant women will develop some red stretch marks on their thighs, stomach or breasts. In time, these should fade to silvery streaks. You can try to avoid them or, at least, minimize them by doing the following:

- Avoid putting on weight too rapidly.
- Eat a healthy, nutritious diet.
- Wear a well-fitting bra to prevent breasts sagging.
- Do regular, gentle exercise.
- Massage with aromatherapy oils containing geranium, mandarin or neroli.

FEELING BETTER THAN EVER

Now is the time when many women report that they feel better than ever! You may feel really energetic and full of vitality as well as being excited about the new life that is developing inside you. Although your waistline is expanding fast and your pregnancy is now visible for everyone to see, your abdomen is still not large enough to cause discomfort. Hormonal changes mean that your skin may be glowing and radiant, and your hair may be thicker, softer and more glossy than usual. Your friends may comment on how well you look.

$\mathcal{Y}$OU & YOUR BABY

YOU are now coming to the end of the second trimester of your pregnancy and you may be starting to feel tired. You will notice the urge to pass urine more frequently as the growing baby starts to press on your bladder. As your "bump" gets ever larger, sleeping will become more difficult because few positions are comfortable. Try lying on your side with one leg bent, supported by a cushion, and the other stretched out.

YOUR BABY is maturing and continuing to gain weight. As the subcutaneous fat builds up under his skin, he is getting plumper and his wrinkles are disappearing. His eyelids have opened and he can now see and focus inside the uterus — he is aware of darkness and light.

BABY IN WOMB

His hands are fully formed

WEIGHT AND LENGTH
Your baby weighs about 1.5kg (3lb) and measures around 28cm (11in) from crown to rump.

WEEK
27

Date 17th March 2000

My thoughts and feelings I am looking forward to seeing the midwife next week. I haven't seen her for 2 months and and I would like to know has I am doing. Tom and I also want to talk about the home birth very much.

Remember If you are finding it difficult to get to sleep, have a hot, milky drink at bedtime.

<table>
<tr><td>WEEK
28</td><td>*Date* 24 March 2000
My thoughts and feelings The midwife</td></tr>
</table>

came to the house today for my 28 week check and to talk about the home birth. Tom came back from work to see her too. Everything with us is normal blood presure extra, and I and 28 cm at ~~weeks~~ 28 weeks very good. The midewife was very posotive about the home birth and Tom and I feel very good about it.

YOUR BABY'S MOVEMENTS

This is the last month in which your baby will be able to turn a somersault inside the womb. He is now quite large with the proportions of a newborn baby, and there is less space for him to move around freely. Consequently, he will reduce his gymnastics and confine himself to just wriggling and kicking.

HIS POSITION

When your doctor or midwife examines your abdomen, they should be able to assess the position of your baby. He will probably continue lying head upwards in the uterus for the coming month, but may turn upside down and "engage" in a head-down position.

EASING HEARTBURN

Now that your abdomen is getting much bigger, you may experience heartburn — an unpleasant burning sensation in your chest just behind the breastbone, sometimes with regurgitation of the stomach acid into the mouth. Heartburn often happens when you lie down, especially when you go to bed at night. Therefore it is a good idea to sleep with your head and shoulders raised and supported by several pillows. A milky drink at bedtime may help neutralize acidity in your stomach. It may also happen when you are lifting heavy weights or coughing. To prevent heartburn, eat little and often; "graze" through the day with smaller meals than usual. Do not eat rich, spicy or fried foods which may upset your stomach. Stick to simple, nutritious snacks and blander flavours.

PREVENTING HEARTBURN
Avoid large meals and eat small, frequent, nutritious snacks instead throughout the day.

BREATHING RHYTHMS

By now you should have joined an antenatal class and be practising your breathing for childbirth. Learning to control your breathing can help you to relax and to ride the contractions, enabling you to push your baby out. Breathe slowly and fully when a contraction starts, then more rapidly as it gets stronger.

DEALING WITH CRAMPS

Cramps are painful contractions of the muscles in the thighs, calves or feet. They often strike at night and waken you from sleep. They may be caused by a salt deficiency or by low calcium levels in the blood. Ask your doctor.

TAKING ACTION

Massage the affected leg or foot firmly and vigorously. Flex your foot upwards towards you, pressing your heel down into the ground. When the pain has eased, walk around to improve the circulation in your feet and legs. For foot cramps, sit with the affected foot and leg outstretched and make gentle circling movements with your lower leg.

WEEK 29

Date 31 march 2000

My thoughts and feelings

Tom and I had a long weekend in Eastbourne. We spent Thursday night at Matt + Rebecca's house, then Tom had his tooth dun an we spent the friday night at Sadies. Saturday and sunday night at Richard and Sara. They had there garc dun quite tense. They we to a fancy dress party an we went visiting on the sunday. Very bad jerney home, we were held up fo an hour and a half in traffi

36

Date ....

My thoughts and feelings ....

I was 30 weeks on the 7th of April. It took a long time to get over the trip to Eastbourne. I am very tired again and have sleeped nearly every day this week. Tom has been in Brussels for 3 days and has worked all weekend. We still can't use the shower.

Remember *If you suffer from cramps, tell your doctor — you may need extra calcium, salt or vitamin D.*

MAKE TIME TO RELAX

As you get larger and heavier in the last trimester of your pregnancy, it is more important than ever to make time for relaxation. As well as just resting and taking the weight off your feet, you should also learn the art of positive relaxation to release physical and mental tension.

TENSE AND RELAX
The tense and relax technique is good preparation for labour. Lie on your back, with cushions behind your head. Breathe in and out slowly, focusing on your breathing and clearing anxious thoughts from your mind. Now think about your right hand: tense it and then relax it. Work up the right arm, then the left arm, tensing and relaxing as you go. Then work down your body to your feet. Finally, relax the muscles of your neck and head. You should feel totally relaxed.

GET PLENTY OF REST
As your pregnancy progresses, you may want to take a siesta every day. Just put your feet up or go to bed.

𝒴OU & YOUR BABY

YOU will attend the antenatal clinic more frequently from now onwards, to have your blood pressure monitored and the baby's position checked.

YOUR BABY is now perfectly formed but is still gaining weight in readiness for birth. Her skin is smooth and pink, she has fingernails and may have a lot of hair. Although she is quite well developed, her lungs still need to adjust to respiration outside the womb. If she was born now, she would probably have difficulty in breathing, although her survival chances would be excellent.

BABY IN WOMB

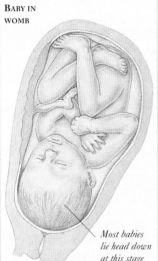

Most babies lie head down at this stage

WEIGHT AND LENGTH
Your baby weighs about 2.5kg (5lb) and measures around 32cm (12in) from crown to rump.

WEEK 31

Date 14ᵗʰ April 2000

My thoughts and feelings Not a good week. Work at Castle View Nursary is now very hard and tires me out comple[tely] I have become very emotio[nal] and can cry at everything, and do. Tom is working long hours and I miss him. I have been to a breast feeding class it was a lot better than I thought it woul[d] be and N.H.S antinatal classes start this week.

HOW YOUR BABY IS LYING

Most babies turn head-down in the uterus by 32 weeks and they stay that way until birth. However, a few stay head-up for a little longer, and a minority will remain like this and will be born in a "breech" (bottom-down) position. When your baby has turned head-down, you will feel her feet kicking your ribs, whereas her head may bounce against your pelvic floor muscles. You may even be able to see your baby moving around now by studying the shape of your abdomen and navel.

Date 21st April 2000

My thoughts and feelings This is my last week at work. It's a short week because of Easter (bank holiday monday) I also went to the R.V.I on Wednesday morning to swap my care from Sunderland. We saw a very nice consultant who has had a home birth of his own. I don't have to go back untill 4 weeks. 17 of us went out for a meal for my leaving do. It was lovely. I got some lovely presents and vouchers and flowers.

Remember *Even though you are getting heavier, you can continue keeping fit by walking and swimming.*

PLANNING FOR YOUR BABY

Now is the time to start preparing for your baby. You can get the nursery ready by doing any necessary decorating and painting, putting up shelves, and fitting a dimmer switch to the overhead lighting system. Start buying some of the baby equipment that you will need — a cot, a carry cot, lay-back buggy or pram, and a portable baby chair. Shopping for baby clothes and accessories can be fun, and will help you to bond with your unborn child. To avoid fatigue, do your preparations in short bursts of activity rather than all at once.

ROCK-A-BYE BABY
A crib that you can rock will make a good first bed for your baby.

PACKING YOUR SUITCASE

This is a good time to get everything ready that you will need in labour, especially if you are going to hospital. Don't take too many things as there may not be much storage space. All you need are basic night clothes, washing things and comfort aids for labour. Pack your bag now so you won't forget anything in the rush when labour starts.

ESSENTIAL ITEMS
sponge bag
2 or 3 nighties
slippers
pants and socks
dressing gown
sanitary pads
nursing bra
towel and flannels
breast pads
tissues
hair care items

WEEK
33

Date 28th April 2000

My thoughts and feelings first week at home. It's Lovely, better than I thought it would be. I can do things at my own pace. I started the N.C.T Antinatol classes this week there was only two couples there very disapointing, there should be some else next week (I hope). The N.H.S classes a very good there are six couples and the groups are friendly a fun. I am also meeting the team of midwifes who will be deliver you. ~~See~~ Sandra our ~~mide wife~~

Remember *Ask your partner to massage your spine gently to ease out aches and pains in the lower back.*

Date 5th May 2000

My thoughts and feelings I saw Sandra on the 8th May she said you are spot on 34 cm and everything else was perfect too. I had an awful night the night before. I had an upset tummy and then very strong Braxton Hix contractions for two hours every 15 minutes and then again at 4 am in the morning. My tummy was saw most of the week went to Bumps + Babes on thursday - the first time. All of the woman 35 + and not really my sort of son, but I shall go again.

PREPARING FOR LABOUR
This position may help relieve the pain of contractions during your labour.

AVOIDING BACKACHE

You are more likely to suffer from backache as your pregnancy progresses and the baby's head engages lower in the pelvis. Don't be tempted to lean backwards to try to compensate for the extra weight. Instead, you should aim to improve your posture and wear low-heeled shoes.

FEELING HEAVY

When you are feeling heavy, you can get some instant relief by kneeling down and leaning forwards with your abdomen supported by a pile of cushions or pillows. This helps take the weight off your back and soothes away any aches and pains. You can also try lying down on your side with your abdomen and the bent knee of your upper leg supported by pillows.

PRACTISING YOUR BREATHING FOR LABOUR

Practise your breathing now to help you cope with the contractions during labour. Sit cross-legged with your back straight and your hands resting on your abdomen. Breathe in and out slowly, relaxing your abdominal muscles as you breathe out. At the peak of a contraction, breathe quickly in shallow breaths.

GETTING A GOOD NIGHT'S SLEEP

You need plenty of sleep during the last trimester but you might find it difficult to get comfortable in bed. A warm bath, a hot milky drink and a soothing massage will all help to relax you.

SLEEPING POSITIONS
Never sleep flat on your back in the last weeks — it could restrict the baby's oxygen supply. Instead, lie on your side, supporting your bent leg with pillows.

WEEK
35

Date 12th May 2000

My thoughts and feelings

I've had a lovely week this week. We had the hall carpet fitted, the dogs had all his hair cut off and we went out for dinner with the couple (who live) behind us. It's the last n.h.s. antinatal class this week, quite sad, I've enjoyed them. I've noted down names and numbers and will phone in a couple of weeks. The N.C.T Breastfeeding class was crap.

COMFORTABLE
POSITION
Extra pillows will help support your body.

Date **19th May 2000**

My thoughts and feelings

Tom was home all weekend
it was lovely. He's got the
shelfs in the utility room dune.
and been great compainy. I've
not felt to good. We had
Nick + Lesley for dinne saturday
night and I sleeped all most the
whole of sunday through I've
lt quite low at the begining of
is week. The home birthing
t arrived on monday we still
eed the gastair and tens machine
ut thats it. Sandra said your
nd. Whent to Pauline's house
ednesday night which lifted my
irits and made me fell less alone.

Remember **If you haven't already
done so, pack your bag in
readiness for hospital.**

YOU & YOUR BABY

YOU will now feel very heavy, and will be longing for the birth of your baby. His head should engage in your pelvis very shortly, and this will relieve some discomfort and heaviness. Colostrum — the early protein-rich breast milk — may start leaking from your nipples.

YOUR BABY is almost ready for birth. All he has to do now is to put on some more fat to help regulate his body temperature after the birth. Inside the womb, he is moving less as he has taken up nearly all the available space. However, you will feel him hiccuping and kicking.

BABY IN WOMB

Hair can be up to 5cm (2in) long

The skin is covered with vernix

WEIGHT AND LENGTH
Your baby is now quite plump and weighs about 3kg (6lb). He is nearly 35cm (14in) long from crown to rump.

𝒫OSITIONS FOR LABOUR

Practise the various positions for labour now so that you can find out which ones are the most comfortable and relaxing. You may want to walk about during the first stage of labour, but as the contractions get stronger you may need to sit, squat or kneel.

SITTING FORWARDS
Many women find this position comfortable early on in their labour. Sit facing the back of a chair with your legs straddled on either side. Lean over the chair back, using a pillow to support your head and arms. Rest your head on your folded arms. T̲ s position enables you ᵗᵒ stay relatively upright.

Head rests on arms

Lean forwards against pillow

WEEK
37

Date 26ᵗʰ May 2000

My thoughts and feelings

Remember Think positively about labour — each contraction is one step nearer to your baby.

44

Date

....

My thoughts and feelings

....

....

....

....

....

....

....

....

....

....

....

APPROACHING BIRTH

The big day when you eventually meet your baby in the flesh is approaching fast, and you are probably feeling very impatient. This is the time when many first-time mothers start to worry about labour and whether they will be able to cope. The antenatal classes should have helped to prepare you, along with the breathing exercises and relaxation techniques you have rehearsed. The more relaxed you feel and the fitter and healthier you are, the greater the chances are of an easy, smooth labour and birth. Don't worry — the months of waiting and preparing for your baby's birth are nearly over.

AROMATHERAPY TO RELAX YOU

Massage with essential plant oils can be very relaxing during your pregnancy. Aromatherapy is a holistic therapy that relaxes the mind and spirit as well as treating the body to promote physical well-being. However, do be aware that some aromatherapy oils are not recommended for use during your pregnancy; if in doubt, you should always ask a qualified professional for advice. The following oils should always be avoided during pregnancy because they are too astringent: basil, bay, clary sage, hyssop, juniper, marjoram, myrrh, pine, sage and thyme.

OILS YOU CAN USE

Every essential oil has its own distinctive fragrance, specific action and special properties. The essential oils that are recommended in pregnancy include citrus oils, geranium, lavender, neroli, rose and sandalwood. Never apply the oils neat — mix just 5–10 drops of your preferred essential oil with a carrier oil, such as wheatgerm or almond oil. Apply the oil with warm hands directly on the skin and massage gently.

COMFORT AIDS FOR LABOUR

Date
....

My thoughts and feelings
....

There are several items that you can take to hospital with you to help relax you and to make your labour more comfortable. Make sure that you pack these in advance; don't leave it to the last minute when they will get forgotten in the excitement.

PACKING LIST
hot water bottle
small natural sponge
water spray bottle
soothing lip balm
back massager
thick, warm socks
music for relaxation

SIGNS OF LABOUR

You may confuse the early contractions in the first stage of labour with the practice Braxton Hicks' contractions that you have experienced.

ONSET OF LABOUR
Labour can start in different ways. These include:
• Contractions that resemble dull backache or strong period pains, becoming more regular with increasing length.
• A show — a plug of thick, blood-stained mucus passing out of the vagina.
• Your waters breaking — the bag of fluid surrounding the baby ruptures.

Date
....

My thoughts and feelings
....

....

....

....

....

....

....

....

....

....

....

....

....

Remember *If you're getting really impatient and fed up with waiting, remember, no pregnancy lasts forever and it won't be long now before you meet your baby.*

$\mathscr{Y}$OU & YOUR BABY

YOU are now ready for the birth of your child, and your body will be sending you signals that it is preparing for labour. The Braxton Hicks' contractions may be more frequent and intense, and you may experience a range of emotions, ranging from anxiety to contentment.

YOUR BABY is now fully mature and fits very snugly inside your uterus with little room for manoeuvre. Her head has settled deeply into your pelvis ready for delivery.

BABY IN WOMB

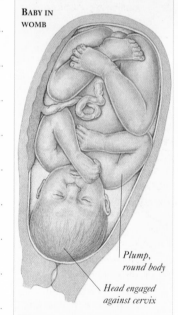

Plump, round body

Head engaged against cervix

WEIGHT AND LENGTH
Your baby is now about 37cm (15in) from crown to rump, and weighs about 3–4kg (6–8lb).

GOING OVERDUE

⑦OES BEING OVERDUE MATTER?

Research has shown that most apparently overdue pregnancies are not late at all — the time of conception has just been calculated wrongly. However, most doctors still become concerned if the pregnancy continues beyond the forty-second week and they may well advise induction.

Most babies grow steadily well into their tenth month in the uterus, but the placenta is now starting to age, and the womb may no longer be the ideal place for the baby. As the placenta becomes less efficient, it may fail to supply adequate oxygen and nutrients to the baby.

An overdue baby who has spent some time in this environment is "post-mature". He may be very thin with dry, peeling skin. He will have longer nails and more hair than other newborn babies.

ONLY A FEW WOMEN GIVE BIRTH on their due date. Most babies are born within two weeks on either side of the estimated delivery date. Don't be disappointed if the big day arrives at last and your baby doesn't! No pregnancy lasts forever and it is only a matter of days before the waiting is over and your baby is born.

My thoughts and feelings
....
....
....
....
....
....
....
....
....
....
....
....

Remember *Your doctor will monitor the situation carefully, and will consider the accuracy of your due date and the health of your baby.*

ℐNDUCING LABOUR

If you are one or two weeks past your due date and there are signs that your baby is distressed, or your placenta has started to fail, or if you have high blood pressure, you may be induced. This means that the labour is started artificially.

There are three induction methods that hospitals use:
• A pessary is inserted into your vagina.
• Your waters are broken.
• You are given a hormone, via an intravenous drip, to make your womb contract.

PRESENTATION FOR LABOUR

The way your baby is lying (the presentation) can affect your labour. The most common presentation is with the baby's spine facing outwards. However, sometimes the baby's head faces outwards, with his spine against yours. Most babies rotate naturally to the correct position before they pass through the birth canal. Some babies present in the breech position and are born feet first.

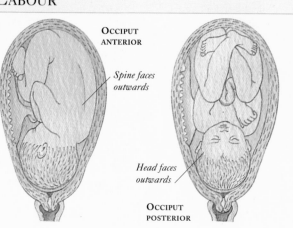

OCCIPUT
ANTERIOR

Spine faces outwards

Head faces outwards

OCCIPUT
POSTERIOR

$\mathcal{W}$RITING YOUR BIRTH PLAN

A BIRTH PLAN IS A WRITTEN LETTER or list that you make, outlining your preferences for the sort of birth that you would like. It should be a comprehensive document, covering everything from pain relief and procedures in labour, to contingency plans if problems arise.

WRITING A BIRTH PLAN

THINGS TO CONSIDER	ISSUES
Your birth partner	• Who will be your birth partner: your partner, a friend or relative? Can you have more than one person? Do you want your birth partner to leave if you have stitches or a Caesarean?
The first stage	• Do you want to be induced if you go past your due date? • Do you want an active labour? • How do you feel about fetal monitoring? • Do you want coaching in breathing and relaxation techniques to relieve the pain in labour? • Do you object to student doctors, midwives or nurses being present? • Do you want to be offered pain relief? • Do you have preferences for pain relief?
The second stage	• In what position would you prefer to deliver your baby? • Would you prefer to tear naturally or to have an episiotomy? • Would you like to see your baby's head delivered? • Would you like your birth partner to cut the cord? • Would you like your baby delivered on to your abdomen? • Do you want help with breastfeeding? • Would you and your partner prefer to be left alone with your baby for a short while after the birth?
The third stage	• Would you prefer to deliver the placenta naturally? • How soon would you like to leave the hospital?

Q Who would you like with you at the birth?

Q What is the most important thing to you about your labour?

Q Do you want to be kept informed and share in any decisions made?

Q Are there any things you would like to have in the birth room?

Q What labour procedure do you want?

Q Have you any special requests about the delivery?

Q Do you want the third stage to be speeded up artificially?

Q Do you want to be alone with your baby after the birth?

Q How do you want to feed your baby?

Q Do you want to be woken at night to feed your baby?

Q What other things are important to you after the birth?

Q Would you like your baby with you, or in the nursery?

MY BIRTH RECORD

Date and time of birth 2-7-2000   5·59 pm   Sunday

Place of birth **Royal Victoria Hospital**

Who was with me **Daddy, The midwife and two doctors**

Pain relief method

Baby's vital statistics – weight, head circumference, length

9lb   4·08 kg weight

14in   37cm head circumference

Apgar score – at 1 minute, at 5 minutes

Baby's appearance **Very br**

Eyes **blue**

Hair **light brown and short**

Looks like **Daddy.**

You've got a chubby face with a long slim body.

My reaction

Father's reaction You are the most wonderful thing that I have ever seen. I was truely speechless, and surprised you were a girl (Mum was convinced you would be a boy)

Other family members' reaction

Baby's photograph

53

𝒫REPARING FOR YOUR BABY

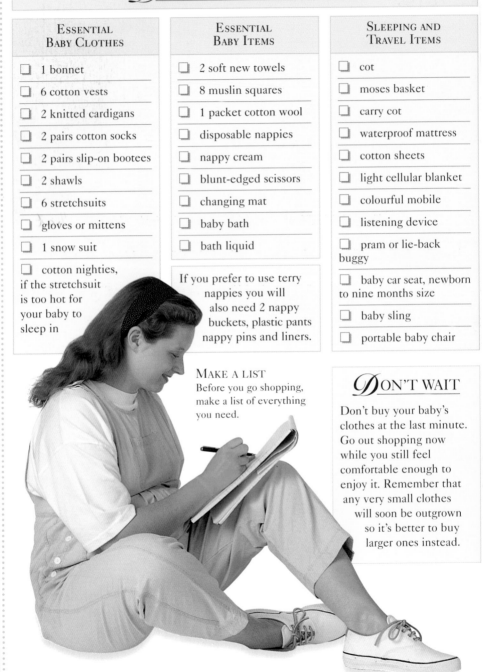

ESSENTIAL BABY CLOTHES	ESSENTIAL BABY ITEMS	SLEEPING AND TRAVEL ITEMS
❑ 1 bonnet	❑ 2 soft new towels	❑ cot
❑ 6 cotton vests	❑ 8 muslin squares	❑ moses basket
❑ 2 knitted cardigans	❑ 1 packet cotton wool	❑ carry cot
❑ 2 pairs cotton socks	❑ disposable nappies	❑ waterproof mattress
❑ 2 pairs slip-on bootees	❑ nappy cream	❑ cotton sheets
❑ 2 shawls	❑ blunt-edged scissors	❑ light cellular blanket
❑ 6 stretchsuits	❑ changing mat	❑ colourful mobile
❑ gloves or mittens	❑ baby bath	❑ listening device
❑ 1 snow suit	❑ bath liquid	❑ pram or lie-back buggy
❑ cotton nighties, if the stretchsuit is too hot for your baby to sleep in	If you prefer to use terry nappies you will also need 2 nappy buckets, plastic pants nappy pins and liners.	❑ baby car seat, newborn to nine months size
		❑ baby sling
		❑ portable baby chair

MAKE A LIST
Before you go shopping, make a list of everything you need.

𝒟ON'T WAIT

Don't buy your baby's clothes at the last minute. Go out shopping now while you still feel comfortable enough to enjoy it. Remember that any very small clothes will soon be outgrown so it's better to buy larger ones instead.

NOTES

Rights and benefits

IF YOU HAVE WORKED for the same employer for at least 26 weeks by the 15th week before your baby is due, you are entitled to Statutory Maternity Pay (SMP) and a total of 14 weeks' leave. If you have two years' service by the 11th week before your baby is due, you are entitled to SMP and 40 weeks' leave. If you aren't entitled to SMP, enquire about Maternity Allowance.

KNOW YOUR RIGHTS

WHEN	WHAT YOU NEED TO DO	WHY YOU NEED TO DO IT
WHEN PREGNANCY IS CONFIRMED	If you're working, inform your employer. If you're not entitled to Statutory Maternity Pay (SMP), find out about Maternity Allowance (MA).	To establish eligibility for SMP and so that you can organize paid time off for antenatal visits.
3 WEEKS BEFORE FINISHING WORK	Confirm to your employer, in writing, when you intend to stop work and your intention to return.	By confirming your intentions to your employer, you protect your right to return to work and to get SMP.
14 WEEKS BEFORE YOUR BABY IS DUE	Ask your doctor or your midwife for a maternity certificate (form MAT B1; in Northern Ireland, Form MB1).	The maternity certificate must be given to your employer to confirm your right to maternity leave and maternity pay.
11 WEEKS BEFORE YOUR BABY IS DUE	You can claim your SMP and Maternity Allowance once you have stopped work.	This is the earliest date that you are allowed to finish work, start your maternity leave and receive SMP.
AFTER THE BIRTH TO 6 WEEKS	Register the birth by the time your baby is aged 6 weeks (3 weeks in Scotland). Claim child benefit. Register to get a birth certificate, and NHS and child benefit forms.	After six months, child benefit won't be backdated.
7 WEEKS AFTER YOUR BABY WAS DUE	You should write to your employer to confirm that you are intending to return to work.	The letter of confirmation that you intend to return to work protects your right to do so.
3 WEEKS BEFORE RETURNING TO WORK	You should write to your employer at this time to inform him of the actual date that you intend to return to work.	Again, writing to your employer with your return date protects your right to return to work.
29 WEEKS AFTER BIRTH	If you are entitled to 40 weeks' leave, this is the latest date you can return to work.	If you don't go back to work by this date, you may lose your right to return at all.

USEFUL ADDRESSES

ACTIVE BIRTH CENTRE
25 Bickerton Road
London N19 5JT
Tel: 0171 561 9006
*Information and classes on
natural childbirth at home or
in hospital.*

**ASSOCIATION OF
BREASTFEEDING MOTHERS**
PO Box 441
St Albans
Herts AL4 0AS
Tel: 0181 778 4769
*A 24-hour telephone service
supplying names and phone
numbers of a nationwide
breastfeeding counsellor
network.*

**ASSOCIATION FOR
IMPROVEMENTS IN THE
MATERNITY SERVICE
(AIMS)**
40 Kingswood Avenue
London NW6 6LS
Tel: 0181 960 5585
*Information and support about
maternity rights and choices.*

**CAESAREAN SUPPORT
NETWORK**
55 Cooil Drive
Douglas
Isle of Man
Tel: 01624 661269 (after 6 pm)

FORESIGHT
28 The Paddock
Godalming
Surrey GU7 1XD
Tel: 01483 427839

*Pre-pregnancy advice and
consultation on preconceptual
care, infertility and miscarriage.*

**GINGERBREAD NATIONAL
OFFICE**
16–17 Clerkenwell Close
London EC1R 0AA
Tel: 0171 336 8183
*Help and advice for one-parent
families.*

**INDEPENDENT MIDWIVES
ASSOCIATION**
94 Auckland Road
London SE19 2DB
Tel: 0181 406 3172
*Network of independent
midwives offering private care.*

LA LECHE LEAGUE
PO Box BM 3424
London WC1N 3XX
Tel: 0171 242 1278
*Advice and information on
breastfeeding.*

MATERNITY ALLIANCE
45 Beech Street
London EC2P 2LX
Tel: 0171 588 8582
*Information on maternity rights
and benefits.*

**NATIONAL CHILDBIRTH
TRUST**
Alexandra House
Oldham Terrace
London W3 6NH
Tel: 0181 992 8637
*Nationwide antenatal classes
and practical postnatal help.*

**ROYAL COLLEGE OF
MIDWIVES**
15 Mansfield Street
London W1M 0BE
Tel: 0171 580 6523/4/5

**THE TOXOPLASMOSIS
TRUST**
61–71 Collier Street
London N1 9BE
Tel: 0171 713 0663

**TWINS AND MULTIPLE
BIRTH ASSOCIATION**
(TAMBA)
PO Box 30
Little Sutton
South Wirral L66 1TH
Tel: 0151 348 0020
*Offers encouragement and
support for parents before and
after multiple births.*

VEGETARIAN SOCIETY
Parkdale
Dunham Road
Altrincham
Cheshire WA14 4QG
Tel: 0161 928 0793
*Nutritional advice for pregnant
women who are vegetarians.*

WOMEN'S HEALTH
52–54 Featherstone Street
London EC1Y 8RT
Tel: 0171 251 6580
Advice on reproductive health.

$\mathscr{P}$ICTURE GALLERY

My first scan
Date:
....

Leaving hospital   *Date:*
....

First photograph
Date:
....